First Printing 2010
Second Printing 2015
Third Printing 2017

Published and distributed by:

www.noorart.com

Email: Info@noorart.com
www.noorart.com

Printed By Mega Printing in Turkey

ISBN: 9781933269085

الله يحبّني
Allah loves me

تأليف : هديل العباسي
رسوم : فلوة ناظر
Written by: Hadeel Al Abasi
Illustrated by: Flua Nather

الله يحبّني
عطوفاً . . .

Allah loves me
when I am kind

الله يحبّني
قارئاً . . .

Allah loves me
when I am reading

الله يحبّني
شاكراً . . .

Allah loves me
when I am thankful

الله يحبّني
مُفكّراً . . .

Allah loves me
when I am thinking

الله يحبّني
مُساعداً ...

Allah loves me
when I am helping

الله يحِبّني
شُجاعاً . . .

Allah loves me
when I am brave

الله يحبّني
قويّاً . . .

Allah loves me
when I am strong

الله يحبّني
كَريماً . . .

Allah loves me
when I am giving

Allah loves me and I love Allah